The Windmills of H

Anthony Triggs

ISBN 0 903852 36 5

Published by
Milestone Publications
62 Murray Road
Horndean
Hants PO8 9JL

Sponsored by
HOMELINE
The Nationwide Home Selling Service.
"The real alternative to estate agents. And their fees"

Dock Mill, Southsea

"Look there's a windmill!" How many times have you heard that said, perhaps during a car trip or a train journey?

Not so many times, perhaps, as you would have done a few years ago.

Before the Industrial Revolution it would have been almost impossible to find a village or town which did not rely upon a mill of some kind - either a water mill, or the more outstanding windmill.

The flatter parts of England, with sluggish rivers were the areas in which windmills were to be found, which is basically the Eastern half of the country.

These friendly giants ground the wheat into flour and the maize and barley into animal feed, and, on the Broads, they pumped and drained water. Some ground pepper, snuff and even stones for road-making.

Windmills have been in existence in this country since the Twelfth Century. The earliest mill for which there is a record was the one built by Herbert the Dean, at Bury St. Edmunds, Suffolk in 1191, and chronicled by Jocelyn de Brakelond. The Dean's mill however, stood for only a short time, for when the Abbott Samson heard about it he ordered it to be pulled down immediately!

The earliest windmill illustration occurred on the first page of a Psalter, illuminated about 1260-70, the last book to be bought by William Morris in 1896.

These early wooden mills were called post mills, because the box-like body of the mill was supported on a huge vertical post upon which the mill revolved to face the sails into the wind.

This main post was held in an upright position by four quarter-bars which rested on massive horizontal cross trees, which in turn were usually supported by masonry pillars to allow the air to circulate freely beneath the whole structure. In some cases a brick underbuilding, called a round-house, was constructed around the base. This gave more protection for the miller, and increased his storage space.

In order to turn the sails or sweeps into the wind a long wooden beam, called a tiller beam, was fitted to the base of the mill body and this enabled the miller to push his mill around to the right quarter. Sometimes a wheel was fitted to the ground end of the beam to lessen the effort needed for the task, and to make the job even easier, some enterprising millers would harness a cart-horse to the beam.

The sweeps were usually constructed from a simple timber frame rigged with a form of canvas cover, which needed to be reefed to different extents to gain the most benefit from the winds. This action, which is similar to the reefing of boat sails, led to the sweeps being called sails in some parts of the country.

This type of sweep is generally known as the common sweep or sail.

Being of timber construction post mills tended to have a relatively short life. They rotted away, collapsed or were blown down with alarming frequency, but surprisingly there are still a respectable number still to be seen.

In fact, being reasonably light they were often moved from one site to another. In 1797 a post mill was dragged for two miles over the downs from Brighton to Preston by a team of 86 oxen.

The post mill was the only mill design until the middle of the sixteenth century. It was then superseded by the mill type that was based upon the circular section, rather than the square box shape of the post mill.

Wooden members, usually eight in number, tapered to the top of the mill and were covered with weather boarding, which gave the mill a rather slab-sided appearance.

It is because of its supposed resemblance to the farm labourer's traditional dress, that this type of mill is known as a ''smock'' mill.

A crude drawing of an early post mill on a lease for Portsdown windmill, dated 1728. (Courtesy: Hampshire Record Office)

Because of the abundance of timber in England, it took a long time for the brick or stone-built mill to be adopted. The tower mill took the form of a tapered building, usually of round section and because of its obvious strength of construction it enabled mills to be built to far greater heights than before.

In both the smock and the tower mill, the cap carrying the sweeps and running on a geared curb was rotated into the wind instead of the entire mill body. This was originally accomplished by means of a long tail-pole fitted to the cap which the miller had to push around by himself - not a great advantage over the post mill!

However in later years a device using an endless chain running over a gear wheel on the cap was used which made the task a less irksome one.

It wasn't until 1746 that the job was made easier still when Edmund Lee invented the fantail mechanism. This comprised a small fan assembly fitted at right-angles to the main sail, at the rear of the cap, and driving the cap round the curb by means of a worm gear of extremely low ratio.

This fan was actuated by the wind changing its quarter and blowing onto the side of the mill. The fantail blades then revolved driving the worm gear, which in turn moved the cap around until the main sails were facing into the wind once again - and all at no effort to the miller.

Later, Andrew Meikle, who invented the threshing machine, invented another aid to milling - the spring sail, which consisted of louvred blades set at a slight twist in order to increase the power of the wind even more.

In 1807, Sir William Cubitt improved the spring sail by running a rod up through each sweep, each rod connecting to a chain mechanism which automatically adjusted the angle of the blades with the changing force of the wind.

These blades or shutters were connected to a bar controlled by a spring, which meant that they were self-regulating by the power of the wind.

Simply, this meant that the miller could alter the area of sail according to the strength of the wind and accordingly gain the best advantage from it, without having to stop his mill from turning.

However, by the time that progress had begun to show some effect in the windmill industry, the same progress began to overtake it.

Strictly speaking it was the Industrial Revolution that caused the beginning of the end for windmills, but it wasn't until the development of the railway that the situation really showed itself to be on the decline. Travel became easier and less time-consuming and the larger mills could supply flour to larger catchment areas, thus putting many of the small local mills out of business.

Later the Hungarian steel roller was introduced into this country - an advancement that produced purer, whiter flour, with none of the minute pieces of grit from the mill-stones left in it.

Millers who could not afford to install the new rollers soon found that their previously faithful market had changed its loyalties.

Gradually the steam engine, the oil engine and the internal combustion engine removed the need for the wind, and mills had no need to even look like windmills anymore, and as before, any miller who could not afford to install such an engine, soon found himself unable to compete.

The millers retired or died without passing the business on, and hundreds of fine windmills were just left standing to decay, as the elements took their toll.

Usually one of the first parts of a mill to disappear as decay sets in, is the cap. In some cases they were removed on purpose or winter gales took their toll and lifted many away.

Mill caps were constructed in a number of very different designs, and although these designs tend to fall into rough geographical areas, this should not be laid down as a rule to rely on. Mill-wrights moved around the land, and took their cap designs with them, and no doubt brought other designs back with them.

The basic design is the Gable cap, such as the one on the tower mill at Bembridge in the Isle of Wight, and another popular one is called the Boat-shaped cap, because of its resemblance to an upturned dinghy.

Some mills have Conical caps, others Domed caps and some have the deeply-curved dome-shaped cap known as the Ogee cap. This last design can be seen locally in a slightly blunted form at Halnaker, near Chichester in Sussex.

Caps were constructed of many different materials - copper, lead or the tarred canvas on boards, which is known as "Marouflage".

The tower mill at High Ham in Somerset has a very original cap, and is the only one of its type in the country - it is thatched.

Nowadays, with the preservation of a large number of mills, their importance to our industrial history is beginning to be realised by the general public, who often subscribe generously to the various funds aimed at keeping at least some of our windmills in good condition.

The windmill on the hill has always been and will continue to be a picturesque sight, and has provided inspiration to many artists and photographers.

It is heartening to see these giants of industry still standing, and giants they most certainly were.

The American poet Henry Longfellow put this thought into verse, and it is a fitting way to end this introduction, before the windmills of Hampshire are looked at more closely.

Behold! a giant am I,
Aloft here in my tower,
With my granite jaws I devour
The maize and the wheat and the rye,
And grind them into flour.

I look down over the farms;
In the fields of grain I see
The harvest that is to be,
And I fling to the air my arms,
For I know it is all for me.

Hampshire has never really been a windmill county, since its long chalky rivers have always provided enough power, putting watermills well to the fore.

A recent report showed that even today the existing watermills in the county outnumber windmills by over ten to one. Many of the windmills that once stood in Hampshire were probably too small to be of any consequence - often standing for such short periods that they have left no record of their passing. Unfortunately, details of the longer-standing mills are nearly as scarce.

A number of windmills stood along the coastline near Lymington, a tower mill stood at Buckler's Hard and another at Fawley. This last one stood until the turn of the century.

Gilbert White, in his "Natural History of Selbourne" mentions a windmill in his area that had disappeared even then and he also includes a view of the village from Windmill Hill.

There is another Windmill Hill at Stockbridge and The Windmill is seen on modern Ordnance Survey maps at Hythe near Southampton. This mill was called Langdown Mill, and all that remains is a flight of steps in the garden of a house, called "Mill Steps".

The city of Southampton itself has had its share of windmills. In 1550 the Court Leet commanded one Thomas Wykes to "scoure his ditch in Kayneshut by the Wyndmille by Michaelmas upon pain of 3/4d".

This mill was later taken over by a Mr. Caplin and by 1612 a lease had been granted to Denis Rowse for 90 years for "the Wyndmille and a voyde plot of ground".

By 1771 the mill had disappeared. The site was where the present-day Regent Street (formerly Caneshut Lane) stands. Another windmill is mentioned in 1600, but no further details are available. There is also very little written about the Castle windmill which supplied flour to Simnel Street, when that area was the bakers' quarter.

The old tower mill at Fawley

Another mill stood on the causeway across the salt marsh and in 1600 it is recorded that the public collected funds to mend the highway from the windmill to the Itchen Ferry.

By 1800 the area around Gosport boasted four windmills. One stood at Haslar, on Tragedy Bank opposite Fort Blockhouse, probably replacing an earlier mill, which together with the mill farm was demolished in 1746, when Haslar Hospital was being built.

The second stood near Crofton Church, and the third at Peel Common.

Mr. Roy Beckingham, who lives in Windmill Cottage, opposite the mill site, remembers it being used as a store-house for beer in the last years of its life before it was finally pulled down.

A tower mill also stood near Ann's Hill in Gosport itself, and in its day it supplied the Royal Navy with flour.

Peel Common mill in its working days

A later picture of Peel Common mill, showing it without sails. (Courtesy: Roy Beckingham)

Grain barges were towed up Forton Creek and the flour returned in the same manner.

The records show that in 1853 a lad of 16 named George Deacon fell from the mill whilst attending to the sails and was seriously injured. He was buried in St. John's churchyard following his subsequent death on June 20th, 1854.

It is perhaps interesting to note that the modern slang word 'nipper', meaning a small boy, is generally supposed to have derived from the name given to millers' apprentices, who were required to 'nip' up and down the sails, to furl and unfurl the canvas. Regrettably, deaths of this kind must have been all too common.

Martin Snape, the well known Gosport artist, painted the mill. Snape, who died in 1930 and is buried in Rowner Churchyard, also painted the Dock Mill at Portsmouth.

Martin Snape's painting of the Ann's Hill mill, Gosport (Original in Gosport Museum collection)

The map of Hampshire as executed by Isaac Taylor in 1759 clearly shows a post mill at Fareham and another, known as Burrant windmill between Fareham and Portchester.

Portchester itself boasted two windmills - the stump of one still stands in private grounds along the foreshore near Portchester Castle. The other, the Wicor Mill was demolished around 1920, and the site is now occupied by the Midland Cattle Produce Ltd.'s factory. Nothing remains of the mill except the faint outline of the foundations, which show it to have been hexagonal in section, and no old pictures have come to light to decide the matter.

The Hampshire Telegraph of January 29, 1821 carried the following advertisement:

WICOR MILL, To let - Wicor Mill, which drives two pairs of stones and is situated on the seashore between Portchester and Fareham, the mill house is large and the out-offices commodius. Application to be made to Mr. Pearce, Mile End, or Mr. J. Ivemy, Buckland, Portsea.

Cornaway Lane still runs from the main Fareham-Portsmouth road and in the past the name probably had a very literal meaning.

Moving slightly northwards, there was a mill on Portsdown Hill, near Fort Widley and Mill Lane is all that is left in memory. A rare print of Widley Windmill will be found in *"Fairdays and Tramdays"*, The Story of Cosham", number 7 in the *Down Memory Lane* series.

A windmill also stood at Waterlooville - and like a great many others was destroyed by fire - on Monday, June 25th, 1906. The Hampshire Telegraph of Saturday, June 30th 1906 carried the following news report:

The truncated stump of the mill on the foreshore at Portchester

"FIRE AT WATERLOOVILLE - Hall's Mill destroyed. Hall's Mill, an old wooden structure standing at the entrance to the village of Waterlooville, was on Monday destroyed by fire. It belonged to Mr. Hall, timber merchant, and was very old, its wooden beams being consequently dry, while a quantity of timber was also stored inside it, this affording additional food for the flames.

Marlands Mill, at West Meon, probably dating from the 17th century.

The remains of the Waterlooville mill after the fire (Courtesy: Miss A. Marshall)

At about noon, when most of the workmen had gone to dinner, the two or three left behind discovered that the building was on fire, and that the flames had already obtained a pretty good hold.

The news was at once conveyed to the village and the Waterlooville Fire Brigade promptly turned out, but by the time it arrived the building was well alight and the flames roaring fiercely.

Fortunately the wind was blowing from the west, so that the fire was carried away from a building alongside the mill, in which most of the machinery had been placed, and where there was some more of the timber stored. The efforts of the brigade were devoted to the saving of this building, and it was evidently hopeless to try and save the mill itself; thanks to the wind being in the right direction, the firemen were successful.

By a quarter past one the flames had been got well under control, but the mill was completely gutted and a quantity of machinery, with the timber stored there was all destroyed.

The loss will therefore, be considerable.

A large crowd soon gathered to watch the flames and there were plenty of helpers. During the operation, a man (not a member of the brigade) who was assisting, narrowly escaped being struck by a falling beam.

Such is the death of a windmill - all over in an hour and a quarter!"

Moving even more to the north we reach Froxfield, near Petersfield. A tower mill once stood here and it was well-described in the following notice from the Hampshire Chronicle of Monday September 8th 1828:

"TO BE SOLD by auction by Messrs. Hollis and Son, at the Jolly Trooper on the Barnet, Froxfield on Friday, September 12th at two-o-clock, under conditions to be there and then produced.

LOT 1. A substantial brick and stone windmill, called Froxfield Windmill, four stories high with a dorae roof, measuring in width on the base 21ft. 6ins., driving two pairs of stones and dressing mill, with the tackle, machinery and furniture, a newly built stable for four horses with loft over and cart house adjoining; a newly built cottage with kitchen, bedroom, pantry, cellar and garden and several closes of good arable land."

The same newspaper carried another advertisement in a slightly later issue - September 28th, 1828 - for another windmill at Dummer, near Basingstoke. It read:

"TO BE SOLD by auction a very compact and valuable estate in the parish of Dummer, near Basingstoke.... a capital windmill, driving two pairs of stones and completely fitted up with a flour machine, grist ditto and bolting mill."

At West Meon, the remains of a stone tower mill, called Marlands Mill, still stand in the gardens of a private house.

Moving southwards again, the old mill at Chalton, overlooking the Portsmouth to Petersfield road is a landmark. For many years the mill stood in a decaying state, although now, fortunately, it has been renovated and converted into living accommodation, and is now a credit to its new owners.

The mill itself was built at the beginning of the last century, but it is said that a series of mills have stood in the same position since the year 1289, thus making the site the oldest in the country.

The land was once part of the manor of Earl Godwin, father of the ill-fated King Harold.

The mill has not been used since the beginning of the century - the last miller being a Mr. Saxby.

For many years the mill stood derelict, with the metal curb still in place, together with part of the fantail staging. Also in position was the main shaft and some of the internal wooden equipment.

In 1973 the mill was offered for sale by auction by the then owner, Squadron Leader J.D.G. Bishop, who had owned it for the previous ten years, but it failed to reach the reserve price.

It was sold privately a year later to Mr. and Mrs. Paul Wohanka of Kingston-upon-Thames, with planning consent for a dwelling conversion. However it wasn't until 1978 that work started on the conversion. A firm of builders from Clanfield was employed to undertake the work.

The tangled undergrowth around the mill was removed first, and then the complete site was cleared. The ground level of the site was lowered by two feet so that the extension buildings would not be unduly obtrusive, and not detract from the original look of the surroundings.

On Monday October 16th, 1978, a crane lumbered slowly up the hill and the internal machinery and the main shaft were removed through the open top of the mill.

The mill building itself was designed to be used as a sitting-room, with bedrooms on the two floors above, with access by means of an open oak staircase.

Later, the top of the mill was re-capped and false sails added. Now the mill stands proudly on the hill top - a thing of beauty, instead of a decaying ruin.

Back in the Thirties, Chalton mill had an earlier claim to fame, when it became the star of a film.

Cinema audiences nowadays cringe in terror at films like "Jaws" and "Alien", but 50 years ago the horror film to beat all horror films was a three-reel epic called "Terrors".

It was a hit in the 20 or more cinemas open in Portsmouth at the time, and there was good reason for the local interest - many of the cinema-goers packing the three-penny seats had acted as extras in the film. It was made by Sound Film Studios, a company with headquarters in Kingston Crescent, and was the brainchild of Mr. Erle Osborn-Smith, an inventive film-maker of the time.

It told the story of three boys who dug a hole in a quarry and succeed in breaking through to a subterranean world, setting free hundreds of monsters. The quarry was actually a chalk pit on Butser Hill and the nearby mill was used in a sequence of trick photography, when a huge lizard-like reptile wrecks it. The film was a huge success and enjoyed international distribution.

From Chalton - 620 feet above sea-level - once could be seen the revolving sweeps of at least four other windmills. One stood at Weston, south of Petersfield, another at Denmead, and two at Hambledon.

The smock mill at Weston stood on a high brick and stone base within a farm complex. It was a tall mill, with common canvas covered sails and a wide balcony around, so that the miller could furl his sails with ease.

Above: *Clearing the site for the transformation of Chalton mill.*
Below: *The interior of the mill, before the machinery was removed.*
(Courtesy: The News)

Lifting the main shaft out of Chalton mill, prior to renovation. (Courtesy:
Mr. Don Eades)

Building begins. (Courtesy: The News)

Almost completed. The new false sails are put into position. (Courtesy: The News)

A bird's eye view down Chalton Mill prior to the removal of the internal machinery. (Courtesy: Mr. Don Eades)

Chalton mill in the thirties, photographed by Rex Wailes.

Hambledon Mill about 1920, already overgrown and ivy covered.

Hambledon mill in the thirties. (Courtesy: Mr. Douglas White)

Weston Mill, early in the century. Courtesy: Mrs. B.M. Wardle)

*Weston Mill during demolition. The cable running to the traction engine can
be clearly seen.* (Courtesy: Miss Olive Seward)

An excellent picture of Denmead windmill - already houses were encroaching upon the farmland. (Courtesy: Mr. D. Coxon)

DENMEAD MILL II

A magnificent view of Denmead mill, taken by Waterlooville photographer C.H.T. Marshall (Courtesy: Miss A. Marshall)

A late picture of Denmead, without sails.

Bursledon windmill, late last century, showing the gallery and farm machinery outside. (Courtesy: Mr. Kevin Stubbs)

The interior of Bursledon mill, showing the wooden machinery

First stage of the renovation of Bursledon Mill - lifting out the old windshaft.
(Courtesy: Mr. Kevin Stubbs)

It was eventually pulled down in 1911, by a traction engine and cable.

The windmill at Denmead was an imposing tower mill and was variously known as the New Denmead Mill, to differentiate it from the older Barn Green Mill, or Gales Mill, from the name of the well-known brewing family who owned it.

According to some sources the mill was built in 1819 and probably worked as a windmill proper until the turn of the century when the sweeps were removed. It stood in this emasculated condition until about 1922, when it was finally demolished by two local men, Charlie Weston and Joe Gardner, with pick-axes and sledge-hammers.

For many years there was a coloured smear on the brick-work, caused by the son of another local man, Arthur Redman, who was painting the woodwork with a colleague when the paint pot was spilled. The mill house is still standing.

Remaining in the southern part of the country we next examine the tower mill, the remains of which stand in private grounds just off the Southampton Road at Bursledon.

A short walk up Windmill Lane is all that is required to see the mill, which was once owned by a local Methodist preacher: Mr. George Gosling. When in working order the mill boasted three pairs of stones, for wheat, oats and barley, all of which were removed in 1930.

The mill was in use until the end of the last century. A corrugated iron roof was fitted, which was used as a viewing platform to see the yachts in the Cowes Regatta. This roof almost certainly added to the preservation of the internal machinery, by keeping the rain out.

The Hampshire Buildings Preservation Trust has now acquired the mill from its former owners, Mr. and Mrs. J.D. Jenkins, and has obtained a lease for a working area on adjacent land. Emergency repairs, to stop further decay, have already been undertaken. It is hoped that the mill will gradually be brought back to working order.

The new cap under construction. (Courtesy: Mr. Eric Lane)

Bursledon Mill in 1981, with the temporary roof in place.

Cast iron machinery was introduced into England from about 1850, and many mills replaced their wooden gears with the newer type. However, Bursledon mill still has much of its wooden machinery, which is gradually being repaired and replaced by local carpenter, Mr. J. Lewis, who was involved in the restoration of the Eling Tide Mill. The external structure is also being renovated, and it is hoped that upon completion the mill will be open to the public on certain days.

The other mill in Hampshire, in addition to Chalton, that has been converted into a dwelling, is the beautiful example at Langstone, near Havant.

It has been a popular subject for artists and photographers for many years - not least its most recent owner, Commander Richard Joicey, whose paintings show the lovely mill to its best advantage.

A combined water and wind mill, it was last at work sometime during the latter part of the last century. An old photograph showing Langstone Harbour completely iced up in 1895 shows the mill to be derelict even then, with its cap and sweeps missing.

Later, in 1927, that indefatigable windmill enthusiast, J.B. Paddon, sketched the mill, showing it to be slightly changed with the odd pieces of fantail debris removed.

Now it carries a fine observation platform with a neat roof, very much in keeping with the windmill atmosphere.

The mill was built on land granted to John Moody, Lord of Havant manor, in about 1730, and was still working in 1857.

At that time the cottage and the granary were separated from the mill itself, but in later years were linked together.

The mill pond, fed by the Lymbourne stream, turned the watermill, which was in use until just before the turn of the century.

All that is left of the watermill is part of the axle and two of the mill stones, which are used as doorsteps in the Royal Oak. A third is built into the mill's flower garden.

Langstone mill in the great freeze of 1895. (Courtesy: Hampshire
County Library)

Langstone Mill in the twenties - how little it has changed!

The men at work removing the gearing of Langstone mill in the thirties.
(Courtesy: Mr. R. Joicey)

At the top. (Courtesy: Mr. R. Joicey)

Although the cottage was used as a dwelling by a Mr. and Mrs. Deadman from just before the first world war, the mill itself was not used until 1932, when it was purchased for £450 by a young artist, Miss Flora Twort, who had moved to Petersfield from Hampstead in 1927.

Miss Twort made the cottage habitable, and then the granary, before she started on the mill. Ernst Freud, son of the famous psycho-analyst, and an eminent architect in his own right, designed some of the interior alterations, and by 1936 the basic work was completed.

The gearing at the top of the mill was removed, and the observation platform with the now-familiar conical cap was fitted. A balcony was also built outside the studio.

Miss Twort lived at the mill until 1948, when it was bought by Mr. and Mrs. Joseph Wade. It was the Wades who united the cottage, granary and mill into one complex, and they also laid the flower garden at the back of the mill.

Mr. and Mrs. Wade were unfortunately killed in a road accident while visiting one of their daughters in South Africa, and the mill was subsequently bought by the noted artist, Richard Joicey.

A Victorian magazine, called "Once a Week", in its issue of January 16th, 1869, carried on its cover an engraving of Langstone Mill, complete with sweeps and cap, and it is interesting to note how little the out-buildings have changed in over a century.

Beneath the engraving was the following text: MILL NEAR HAVANT, LANGSTONE HARBOUR, HANTS, by E. Duncan. A mill dull, plodding, energetic, constant, that by the mobile, multitudinous sea, stood fast with outstretched arms..., and was blown by revolutionary winds, observed routine of duty.

Nearly completed. (Courtesy: Mr. R. Joicey)

Langstone Mill as it is now.

The old engraving showing Langstone Mill with full sail. (Courtesy: Hampshire Record Office)

North Hayling windmill

The mill has always enjoyed a rather infamous reputation owing to early associations with local smuggling activities.

It is said that a tunnel runs underground between the mill and the Royal Oak public house, a short distance away.

Travelling southwards from Langstone we reach Hayling Island, where according to records there were once at least three windmills, the last one being destroyed as late as 1890.

The old Hayling Tide water mill, which stood directly opposite the present Maypole Inn was mentioned as being part of the Hayling Priory as far back as 1294 and was valued at £3. By 1325 the inventory of the Priory mentions another mill, obviously a windmill. In this year a petition was made to the Crown asking for a remission of taxes and a lower valuation of the mills. The petition was heard by Ralph de Bereford and Richard de Westcote, who were described as "wardens of the alien religious house in the County of Southampton". As a result, the value of the mills was dropped to £1 per annum.

The site of the windmill has always been known as Windmill Hill Field, and in the early 1930s during an excavation of a tumulus in the area, Mr. E.S. McEuan came across the remains of what appeared to be two windmills on top of the Neolithic burial place.

The first one could have been the remains of the windmill mentioned above and was obviously a post mill, as the charred remains of the main post cross braces were discovered. Close by, the distinctive cross shape of a later post mill, this time not destroyed by fire, was found.

So far two of the Hayling mills have been accounted for, leaving the famous North Hayling windmill, which was a well known feature of the landscape for many years. Owned by Mr. George Sparkes, it stood as the only mill on the island until it was destroyed by fire in 1890. The Hampshire Telegraph of October 11th, 1890 gave us all the unfortunate details:

Grately Mill early in the century, already no longer working. (Courtesy: National Monuments Record)

"WINDMILL ON FIRE. A fire broke out on Wednesday between ten and eleven o'clock at the Windmill at North Hayling, owned by Mr. Sparkes. It is supposed that the fire was caused by friction in the axle of the fan, as the flames shot out at the top of the mill, and in a short time the fan fell to the ground with a great crash, but happily no one was hurt by the fall. The Havant Fire Brigade were summoned, and, with their fire engine, soon arrived. Mr. Edney, one of the Fire Brigade, who was on the spot, at once worked to husband the water supply by clearing out a ditch, and Mr. G. Jones is deserving of praise for the promptitude in which he conveyed the message to Captain Street, a distance of three miles. The mill was completely burned out, but fortunately was insured."

There is no record of Mr. Sparkes building another mill in the area, so perhaps he used the insurance money for other purposes! The mill house, a two storey white rendered house with a slate roof, however, is still standing.

To the north of the county lies the village of Grately, and here until two or three years ago stood the stub of a tower mill, used until recently as a storehouse. The mill was built in 1849, and lived a short life as a windmill proper, as the sweeps were removed on Easter Monday 1889. A steam engine was then installed, but the boiler burst soon after and an oil engine replaced it. The stub of the shell was demolished only recently.

Just south of Winchester stands Owslebury, which boasted two windmills for a time. The first of these was a tower with common sails, which was said to have been destroyed by enemy action during the First World War. This mill may well have been the last working windmill in the county, if the letter from a correspondent signing himself with the letter 'P', to the Hampshire Independent, February 15th, 1890, is anything to go by.

The construction of Owslebury pumping mill, with the pipes ready to be sunk. (Courtesy: Mr. Geoffrey Bridger)

The same mill in the twenties - a derelict tower.

OWSLEBURY MILL.

Owslebury mill, in the interim period with the small Spanish type sails.
(Courtesy: Mr. Geoffrey Bridger)

Owslebury corn mill - possibly the last working windmill in the county.

33

Rudmore Lime Mill, from a painting in the Portsmouth Museum Collection. (Courtesy: Portsmouth Museum)

An old engraving showing the White Mill at Southsea.

"THE LAST OF THE HAMPSHIRE WINDMILLS. I may not be correct, but my memory does not at the moment supply me with a picture of any other living windmill used for grinding than the one at Owslebury, between Upham and Winchester. I mean as regards the County of Hants. There are several dead windmills in the county - perhaps I know the most of them - one at Hythe, one at Bursledon, one or two in the Isle of Wight, and others - but I feel sorrow in saying that many of the picturesque and old-time windmills are not now in the active life of the living. Owslebury is a place I had not been to till last Tuesday. I had seen its church - high up - and its mill - miles off - but had not been within touch and sound."

The second, known as Bridle's Mill was a pumping mill and had a shaft some hundreds of feet deep sunk below it. When it was first built it boasted a somewhat novel method of harnessing the wind - an annular sail, constructed in the form of a ring with many small blades set inside it. Later photographs show that this sail was removed and an even stranger one was substituted - slightly reminiscent of a Spanish mill, with small triangular sails.

Later still, in 1914, an engine was installed and sail power was completely dispensed with. The bleak tower stood until fairly recently.

Travelling southwards again, we reach the city of Portsmouth, which has had a varied but continuous history of milling.

The earliest record of windmills in Portsmouth is an old map showing a line of them along the top of Portsdown Hill. These were almost certainly tiny post mills - so small, in fact, that the body of the mill only consisted of one room, and there was no roundhouse to cover the trestle and post at the base.

These certainly cannot be listed as mills of any permanence as they were probably blown down and rebuilt many times during the course of the years.

The first mill of any importance was built on the northern shore of Portsmouth Harbour in about the fourteenth century, and apparently had some connection with the tide water mill at Fareham Creek.

A small windmill stood on the site of the present Portsmouth Guildhall, but its history seems to have been very short-lived, as it had disappeared by 1800.

The next to be built was situated at Southsea, near the cattle pond which lay on the site of the present-day Canoe Lake. Known as Lump's Mill, it stood on land belonging to Lump's Farm. According to an ancient deed, one Philip, son of Peter de Eesteneye, held one acre of land at Esteneye (Eastney) under Ralph Lumpe and his wife Cecily.

The mill was a tower mill and because of its colour was commonly known as the White Mill. Milling ceased by about 1850 but the mill itself was still standing until at least 1870.

Ballard's Mill, which stood on the site of the present Queen's Hotel.

An old etching, showing the line of mills at Flathouse

The Queens Hotel of today covers the site of a tower mill which was known as Ballard's Mill, which stood near a farmhouse and a well-known inn.

It was demolished in 1843 in order to build a large house, which itself was removed at a later date when construction of the Queens Hotel was started.

An old engraving shows a line of mills along the coastline of the Stamshaw and Rudmore area. Five windmills could be seen and all were standing by the middle of the nineteenth century. The most northerly was Rudmore Mill, sometimes called Byerly Mill, and below that stood a smaller mill, called Dwarf Mill.

According to contemporary maps this mill was a corn mill, but adjacent to the mill stood a row of kilns. A water colour painting of the time shows the mill but describes it as the Lime Mill. This description may have been made in error by the artist, who after seeing the kilns nearby, jumped to the wrong conclusion - or it might just be that in later years the mill was actually used for powdering lime.

The third mill standing along the coast was Dennison's Mill and below that, but just slightly inland was the Mile End Mill. Mr. Pearce was the miller here for a time, but later Mr. Emery took over, and gradually the mill became known as Emery's Mill.

Finally, the most southerly mill was the Old Dock Mill also called the Shipwright's Mill.

At the close of the eighteenth century bread had become so expensive that to help the poor, the Portsmouth Dockyard shipwrights built their own mill.

This mill, naturally known as the Shipwrights' Mill continued to be a blessing to the poor until 1816, when the owners were informed that the land upon which their mill stood was to be used by the Admiralty to enlarge the dockyard and naval establishments.

It was this action that started the story of the most famous windmill ever to be built in Portsmouth.

The famous Dock Mill.

37

Dock Flour Mills, Southsea. Built 1817.
Last driven by wind 1905, now by engine.
One Million bricks used in construction. No. 746.

Two views of the stately Dock mill

The Dock Mill cottages, prior to restoration.

The fully restored cottages.

The interior of the Dock Mill, whilst under the control of Mr. Maurice Welch.

With the resounding success of their first venture behind them, the shipwrights started a collection and formed the Dockyard Co-operative Mill Society. They then constructed their own new windmill at Southsea and even started a commercial bakery.

The big black windmill, known fondly as the Dock Mill, stood 100ft. high and 40ft. across the base and was said to be the largest of its type in England. The Army Board of Ordnance supplied one million bricks, all of which were used.

The original Shipwrights' Mill now became known as the Old Dock Mill and it is interesting to note that it was still occupied, according to the rate books, well into the middle of the century, obviously still working within the walls of the dockyard.

It is said that the following legend was engraved above the door of the new Dock Mill:

This mill is the equal property of subscribers. 1813.
Both rich and poor, a friend will find.
Who standeth here, their corn to grind.

In spite of its superlatives, the Dockyard Mill Society went to the wall in 1834 as a direct result of increased wages.

The mill itself continued to be worked under a variety of owners, until about 1860. It then stood derelict until 1869 when it was purchased by Mr. Maurice Welch, a miller of renown. He had previously been in charge of the King's Mill, the Admiralty tide mill that stood at the Quay Gate and was destroyed by fire in 1868.

To reach his newly-acquired mill Mr. Welch was forced to build his own road, for the undergrowth had become so thick during the years of neglect.

As soon as he arrived he installed steam power for grinding, with wind as a standby. By 1905 the sails revolved for the last time when wind power was completely dispensed with.

An article printed in the Gentleman's Journal dated November 2nd, 1907 described the mill so well that I make no apologies for including it in full.

"MESSRS. WELCH AND SON. The Dock Mill is one of the most interesting centres of industry in Portsmouth. It was originally built about 1817 by the Dock Mill Society, and the deeds give the position as Southsea Common, but the neighbourhood has since been built over and the boundaries of the common of today are some considerable distance away.

The Dock Mill has been in the possession of Mr. Welch and his family for the past 40 years or so, and during that time a costly equipment of up-to-date milling machinery has been installed. At present the mill is a happy combination of the ancient and the modern - an old-fashioned picturesque exterior with the most advanced appliances within.

Upton Mill, Aldemoor, Isle of Wight. (Courtesy: Mr. Kenneth Major)

Flour milling is an ancient industry, and for many centuries it resisted the introduction of any improved methods. We are indebted to Budapest, in Hungary, for the modern roller system of milling, the old mill stones giving way to steel rollers.

The flour then lost the grit from the mill stones and the discolouration produced by the grinding of the husks of wheat, and for the first time it was produced with beautiful whiteness. The new system found a welcome in America, and later on in England, where vast improvements have been made in the various machines and the methods of working. These improvements are to be found in the Dock Mill, so that all that invention has put upon the market to secure the best flour has been taken advantage of.

The Dock Mill is one of the sights of Southsea. It is a gigantic building; 100 feet high, and is the loftiest mill of its kind in England. Adjoining are buildings comprising wheat cleaning and preparing departments, warehouses, boiler and engine rooms, offices etc.; in fact everything necessary to make the mill self-contained and complete.

The site is an admirable one for receiving grain, whilst the flour and other products of manufacture can be conveniently dispatched by rail or water.

It is interesting to watch the wheat as it passes through the various processes in Mr. Welch's mill. It is elevated into the granary on the third floor of the preparing mill, thence it passes to the separators on the floor beneath where it is graded and all the seeds and foreign matter removed. It again descends to a lower floor, where an elaborate plant of scouring, cleansing and brushing machinery makes it ready for the mill. It is conveyed to the ground floor of the great mill, where are situated the double set of steel rollers. It passes alternately through rollers, purifiers and sifters until every particle of the kernel is removed as a white powdery form. This is delivered into sacks on one floor, whilst the bran or husks are ejected on another.

The whole of this process is entirely automatic, the wheat and its products not being handled from the time it is received till it is filled into sacks in readiness for the baker. Every part of the premises is clean and kept wonderfully free from dust, each room and machine being connected to exhaust fans. These keep the air pure - a condition of vital necessity in the manufacture of an article of food. It speaks well for the superiority of the flour manufactured when we say that at the International Bakeries Exhibition, held in London in 1905, a medal was awarded for the excellent quality of the bread made from their flour.

Again, this year, 1907, two first prizes were awarded for cakes made from their celebrated 'Purity' flour."

The Dock Mill was put up for auction in 1922 but was not sold, and was eventually demolished in 1923 - the last of the windmills of Portsmouth.

The mill cottages, however, are still to be seen. A few years ago they were threatened with demolition because of their poor condition, but they have recently been renovated to such an extent that they are now a showpiece, combining both the ancient and the modern. It is interesting to see the broad-arrow of the Army Ordnance Board stamped into a number of the bricks.

Leaving Portsmouth, we take a final short trip across the Solent to the Isle of Wight.

An early seventeenth century map of the island showed four windmills very clearly, all illustrated by little post mills, which they no doubt were. A large one was shown at Shalcombe and another of considerable size was situated at Cheverton Down. A third was shown at Kington, just north of Newchurch and the last at Shanklin.

By 1682 Captain Grenville Collins was appointed by King Charles II to make a survey of England. When Collins came to surveying the Solent, he wrote: "When the windmill on the Isle of Wight bearest S.W. by W., then you are abreast of the Buoy of Horse".

In recent times the island boasted seven windmills. One stood in the Manor of Walpen at Chale, another at Freshwater, a third at the west side of Ryde, at Mill Fields, and a fourth at Aldemoor, near Ryde.

Cowes boasted two mills - one at the east and the other at the west.

The Chale mill is recorded in the Manor of Walpen as follows: "William Ralegh of Walpen, Chale, had a windmill worth 6s 8d in 8 Henry 4".

The Freshwater site has a long history as there are records of a windmill being there in 1292, so there have probably been a number of mills on or near the same place since then. The last mill on the site was disused by 1863, and was a tower mill.

A stone tower mill stood at Mill Fields, Ryde, near the Newport Road, and another, known as Upton Mill, at Aldemoor, near Ryde. This latter mill stood until 1915.

The windmill at West Cowes was also a tower mill, with common sails. The site is remembered by the mill house, which still stands, and the now derelict Mill Hill railway station. The East Cowes mill was standing in 1759, but had disappeared by 1846.

The remaining mill, Bembridge Mill, still stands and is the property of the National Trust. It was built in 1700 and was situated on Binbridge Isle, now a name of the past owing to the reclamation of Brading Harbour some 80 years ago.

The roof was originally of straw but was replaced with one of wood in 1720.

Inside the 40 foot tower, which has been rendered on the weather side to afford better protection, a beam carries the carved name of one of the mill boys - E. Beker - and the date, 1746 A.C.

Apparently the Pope was so unpopular in England at that time that the English A.C. (After Christ) replaced the usual A.D.

The mill has four levels and the cap is turned into the wind by the endless chain method. It was constructed of local stone upon the orders of the Lord of Yaverland Manor, and worked until about 1914, the last miller being Mr. A. Morris.

Gradually it became more decayed - the inside machinery becoming infested with woodworm and death watch beetle. It was used for a time as a cow shed and a store until the second world war, when the Home Guard took it over as an observation post, during which time lightning destroyed one of the sweeps.

When Mr. Morris died, he left the mill to his niece, Mrs. E. Smith of the nearby Mill Farm. She offered it to the National Trust who accepted it.

In 1958 the Island National Trust Properties Management Committee launched an appeal for restoration funds, which was magnificently subscribed to by many of the island's town councils and private individuals.

Restoration started in 1959 and the mill was actually taken over by the Trust in 1961.

Drawings for new sweeps were prepared by Mr. R.C. Durden and the actual carpentry was done by Mr. F. Cheverton.

The original mill-stones had been removed, but luckily the stones from the now demolished tide mill at Wootton Bridge fitted exactly. The original stones were later discovered in an ornamental garden at St. Helens, the owner having bought them in 1920.

Bembridge windmill is now a showpiece for visitors, and is well worth a journey to see - a fact well supported by the figure

West Cowes windmill, Isle of Wight. (Courtesy: Kenneth Major)

Freshwater windmill. (Courtesy: Mr. Kenneth Major)

43

Bembridge Mill in the thirties, before restoration. (Courtesy: Mr. Rex Wailes)

The present-day Bembridge Mill, under the control of the National Trust, and a showpiece for visitors.

44

showing the actual number of visitors each year.

Bembridge mill is also the most fitting mill upon which to end this short survey of Hampshire mills, as to date it is the only one preserved in its natural state - although Bursledon mill may well rival it in the future. At the moment, then, if you can only take time to see one of the county's mills, then Bembridge is a must.

WINDMILL SPOTTER

There are many other windmills to be seen in the south of England - unfortunately many are ruinous towers, scant remains or conversions. Obviously these are not so pleasing to the eye for the casual spectator, who naturally likes to see something with a certain amount of charm and picturesque quality. However, there are still many beautiful examples to be seen, and the following is a list of those within reasonable distance of Hampshire. The type of mill is given in brackets after each name.

Sussex
Earnley (Smock)
Halnaker (Tower)
High Salvington, Worthing (Post)
Medmerry Mill, Selsey (Tower)
King's Mill, Shipley (Smock)
West Chiltington (Smock)
Patcham, Brighton (Tower)
West Blatchington, Brighton (Smock)
Rye (Smock)
Icklesham, near Rye (Post)
Battle (Smock)
Stone Cross (Tower)
Polegate (Tower)
Rottingdean (Smock)
Nutley (Post)
Clayton (Jack - Tower; Jill - Post)

Oldland (Post)
Chailey Heritage (Smock)
Winchelsea (Post)

Kent
Chillenden (Post)
Meopham (Smock)
Canterbury (Tower)
Rolvenden (Post)
Cranbrook (Smock)
Sandwich (Smock)
Stelling Minnis (Smock)
West Kingsdown (Smock)

Somerset
Chapel Allerton (Tower)
High Ham (Thatched Tower)

Surrey and London
Ewhurst (Tower)
Outwood (Post)
Reigate, Wray Common (Tower)
Reigate Heath (Post)
Upminster (Tower)
Brixton (Tower)
Shirley (Tower)
Wimbledon Common (Hollow Post)

This short list does not pretend to be exhaustive, but it does present some of the better mills, and certainly some of the most photogenic. Anyone who owns a camera will soon find that it can all too easily become an obsession to preserve on film these wonderful examples of England's fast disappearing industrial heritage. But it can be a very enjoyable obsession!

Short Glossary of Windmill Terms

BEDSTONE The lower of the pair of millstones. The fixed stone. See RUNNER STONE

CAP The movable top of a TOWER MILL, which carries the SAILS into the wind by rotating on a geared track or CURB.

CURB The geared ring or track at the top of the mill, upon which the CAP turns.

COMMON SAIL The traditional cloth covered SAIL.

CROSS TREES The horizontal cross shaped main beams in the lower structure of a POST MILL.

FAN TAIL The small fan assembly at the rear of a TOWER MILL, which turns the CAP and SAILS into the wind by gearing connected to the CURB.

MAIN SHAFT The main upright shaft which transmits the power of the wind to the STONES.

PATENT SAIL A remote controlled SAIL with shutters which can be adjusted for best effect, without stopping the mill.

POLL END The cast iron box shaped fitting on the end of the WINDSHAFT, into which the STOCKS are fitted.

POST MILL A mill, the body of which is mounted upon a large upright post, which in turn is held in an upright position by the CROSS TREES.

ROUND HOUSE A building, usually enclosing the sub-structure of a POST MILL, often used for extra storage space.

RUNNER STONE The upper movable stone which rotates upon the BEDSTONE.

SAILS The revolving arms of a mill. See COMMON SAIL, SPRING SAIL, PATENT SAILS and SWEEPS.

SMOCK MILL A timber mill, often of octagonal section, standing usually upon a brick base, and so called because of its supposed resemblance to a country farmer's smock.

SPRING SAIL A SAIL with venetian blind like shutters, which are spring controlled.

STOCKS The timber arms of a windmill, to which the SAILS are fitted.

STONES See BEDSTONE and RUNNER STONE.

SWEEPS See SAILS.

TAIL POLE The long timber lever used to bring the body of a POST MILL, or the CAP of a TOWER MILL into the wind, usually by manual operation.

TILLER BEAM Another term for the TAIL POLE.

TOWER MILL A mill constructed of brick or stone, with a rotating CAP at its top.

WIND SHAFT The axle to which the SAILS are fitted, by means of the POLL END. The shaft is usually set at an angle, downwards towards the rear of the mill, to maintain balance.

SELECT BIBLIOGRAPHY

Specialised bibliography

Gazeteer of the Water, Wind and Tide Mills of Hampshire: C.M. Ellis. (Hampshire Field Club)
Bembridge Windmill: T.R. Parsons. (National Trust)
The Mills of the Isle of Wight: J. Kenneth Major (Charles Skilton)

General bibliography

Discovering Windmills: J.T.N. Vince. (Shire Publications)
The Standing Windmills of West Sussex: Richard and Richard McDermott. (Betford Publications)
Getting to know about Windmills: Jeffery W. Whitelaw. (PhotoPrecision Ltd.)
Somerset Windmills: Martin Watts. (Agraphicus Publications Ltd.)
Upminster Mill: Anthony D. Butler. (Peter Davis)
Windmills in Surrey and Greater London: A.C. Smith. (Stevenage Museums Publication)
The Windmills of Surrey and Inner London: K.G. Farries and M.T. Mason. (Charles Skilton)
Windmills in Sussex: Rev. Peter Hemming (C.W. Daniel and Co.)
The English Windmill: Rex Wailes. (Routledge & Kegan Paul)
The Union Mill, Cranbrook: Peter Ryan. (Charing and District Local History Society)
Windmills of England: Rex Wailes. (Architectural Press)

ACKNOWLEDGMENTS

Since my first article on Hampshire windmills appeared in the now defunct Hampshire Telegraph of November 21st, 1968, I became bitten by the bug and have spent the intervening years continually on the look-out for pictures and information.

There are naturally a number that have come to hand through various sources, for which it is impossible to credit ownership.

I have acknowledged every picture that I am sure of, and offer my apologies for any others not credited.

My thanks must go to a number of individuals, many of whom have become good friends, who have been unstinting in their help. These include: Miss A. Marshall, Douglas White, Geoffrey Bridger, Geoffrey Salter, Roy Beckingham, Arthur Corney, Kevin Stubbs, Eric Lane, Kenneth Major, Rex Wailes and Richard Joicey.

Finally, I give my thanks to my wife Sue, who has generously given her help and encouragement and has cheerfully put up with windmills for many years.

Is this you –
or your Estate Agent?

Saving the £500-£1000 your estate agent would charge to sell an average house or flat could buy you a superb holiday for two. Instead of paying for your estate agent's holiday, you could sell your property through Homeline — at a cost of around £60.

With Homeline, you can sell privately and discreetly, highlighting the features that mean most to you. There are no hidden extras, and **no commission on sale.**

For buyers the service is free — you give us your requirements, and we'll send you details of properties that match, putting you in touch with the seller direct.

Our Hayling Island office covers the Solent area from Bognor Regis to Southampton and extends to Winchester and Midhurst. What estate agent can so effectively give such wide coverage from a single office?

The Homeline service helps you with surveys, mortgages and conveyancing — in fact everything you need when you move. We have offices throughout the Midlands, the West, the South and the London area. For more information **Phone Hayling Island 67142**

Regal House, Mengham Road, Hayling Island, Hants.

Homeline

The real alternative to estate agents. And their fees.

48